THE KRAKKEN

BEN, HIS GRANDPA MAX,
AND COUSIN GWEN, ARE CAMPING BY A LAKE.
THEY SOON HEAR ABOUT A MYSTERIOUS
MONSTER OF THE DEEP ... WHAT DOES IT
WANT, AND CAN BEN'S ALIEN HEROES
HELP SAVE THE DAY?

IT'S NIGHT TIME ...
BEN'S SWIMMING IN A LAKE,
SHOWING OFF IN FRONT OF
GWEN. HE SINKS BELOW THE
WATER ...

"VERY FUNNY BEN, I'M NOT FALLING FOR IT,"
SAYS GWEN.

SUDDENLY, A HUGE
MONSTER COVERED
IN SEAWEED REARS
UP IN FRONT OF
GWEN! *AGGH!* SHE
SCREAMS, AS THE
MONSTER LOOMS
OVER HER. GWEN
FALLS AND DROPS
HER TORCH.

SHE THEN REALISES
IT'S BEN AS ONE OF HIS
ALIENS – *FOUR ARMS!*
"YOU ARE SO BUSTED
WHEN I TELL GRANDPA!"

HA HA HA!

"I CAN'T BELIEVE SHE FELL FOR IT,"
LAUGHS FOUR ARMS. "A MONSTER IN THE
LAKE. HOW DUMB CAN YOU BE?"

THE NEXT MORNING, BEN AND MAX ARE GOING FISHING. GWEN DOESN'T WANT TO GO, SO SHE STAYS BEHIND ON THE PONTOON.

MAX AND BEN FIND THE BOAT THEY'VE CHARTERED AND MEET THE OWNER, A CREEPY GUY CALLED CAPTAIN SHAW.

ON THE BOAT, CAPTAIN SHAW TELLS BEN AND MAX ABOUT THE LAKE MONSTER.

IT'S CALLED THE KRAKKEN, I'VE BEEN ON ITS TAIL FOR YEARS. I COULD HELP YOU FIND THE BEAST — IF YOU'VE GOT THE STOMACH FOR A REAL ADVENTURE?

THEY MOTOR ACROSS THE LAKE TO FIND AN AREA SURROUNDED BY BUOYS, MARKED 'DO NOT ENTER'.

A BOAT COMES TOWARDS THEM, AND A MAN'S VOICE SHOUTS OUT.

STOP WHERE YOU ARE. I'M JONAH MELVILLE, THE FOUNDER OF FRIENDS OF FISH. WE'VE CLOSED THIS SECTION OF THE LAKE FOR AN ENVIRONMENTAL STUDY. YOU'LL HAVE TO TURN AROUND.

BUT WHAT ABOUT THE KRAKKEN?

HA HA, THE KRAKKEN?" JONAH LAUGHS. "NOT THAT OLD FISH STORY. LOOK, I'M A MARINE BIOLOGIST, AND ANYBODY WHO TELLS YOU THEY'VE SEEN A MONSTER IN THIS LAKE IS CASTING WITHOUT A HOOK."

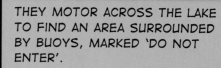

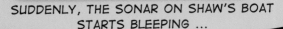

SUDDENLY, THE SONAR ON SHAW'S BOAT STARTS BLEEPING ...

THE SONAR! WE'VE FOUND SOMETHING!

OR SOMETHING'S FOUND US, *LOOK!*

THE LAKE GETS ROUGHER AND ROUGHER UNTIL A MONSTER APPEARS! IT'S *THE KRAKKEN* AND IT'S HEADING STRAIGHT FOR THE PONTOON – AND ALL THE TOURISTS! THE KRAKKEN REARS UP, DWARFING EVERYBODY. IT CRASHES INTO THE PONTOON AND SWEEPS GWEN INTO THE WATER!

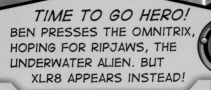

TIME TO GO HERO!
BEN PRESSES THE OMNITRIX, HOPING FOR RIPJAWS, THE UNDERWATER ALIEN. BUT XLR8 APPEARS INSTEAD!

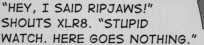

"HEY, I SAID RIPJAWS!" SHOUTS XLR8. "STUPID WATCH. HERE GOES NOTHING."

BUT XLR8 IS AS FAST IN WATER AS HE IS ON LAND! HE ZIPS ALONG THE SURFACE TOWARDS THE BROKEN PONTOON, AND PLUCKS GWEN FROM THE COLD LAKE.

"YOU OK?" XLR8 ASKS GWEN.

I THINK SO, THANKS FOR THE SAVE!

XLR8 RUSHES OFF TO SAVE EVERYONE ELSE.

XLR8 LEAPS ON BOARD JONAH'S BOAT. THE KRAKKEN IS TRYING TO PULL A WOODEN CRATE OUT OF JONAH'S HANDS. BUT XLR8 FIGHTS OFF THE LAKE MONSTER, AND SAVES THE CRATE!

WHAT'S SO IMPORTANT IN THAT CRATE THAT YOU RISKED YOUR LIFE FOR IT?

EH, OUR LUNCH.

XLR8 CAN'T BELIEVE IT. "YOU ALMOST GOT MUNCHED FOR A FEW SANDWICHES?" HE ASKS.

THE KRAKKEN GRABS THE CRATE AGAIN. XLR8 CHASES IT ACROSS THE LAKE, BUT THE OMNITRIX STARTS BLEEPING ... AND XLR8 TURNS BACK INTO A VERY WET BEN!

BACK ON THE SURFACE, SHAW FINDS THREE MYSTERIOUS, MASKED MEN ON HIS BOAT.

I HAVEN'T ANYTHING WORTH STEALING.

AH, BUT YOU HAVE US ALL WRONG, ALL WE WANT IS SOME INFORMATION. LIKE WHAT DID YOU SEE DOWN THERE?

"NOTHING," SAYS SHAW. "SAME AS ALWAYS."

SMACK! THE MAN HITS SHAW IN THE FACE, KNOCKING HIM UNCONSCIOUS. THE MAN PULLS OFF HIS MASK. IT'S JONAH!

STILL IN THE LAKE, BEN HAS SEEN AND HEARD EVERYTHING. HE PRESSES DOWN ON HIS WATCH. IT DOESN'T WORK!

JONAH AND HIS TEAM CARRY SHAW ON TO THEIR OWN BOAT.

FIND OUT IF HE KNOWS ANYTHING BACK AT THE CANNERY.

WE'LL COME BACK LATER TO SNAG THE REST OF THE EGGS!

BOOM! JONAH DESTROYS SHAW'S BOAT WITH AN EXPLOSIVE. HEARING THE EXPLOSION, BEN FRANTICALLY TRIES THE WATCH AGAIN.

IT'S HERO TIME

IT WORKS, AND BEN DECIDES IT'S TIME TO GO STINKFLY! HE CHASES JONAH'S BOAT, BUT HE'S BEEN SEEN, AND THE MEN FIRE AT HIM. DODGING BULLETS, HE FALLS INTO THE WATER ...

A BIT LATER, BACK AT CAMP, THE GANG AND CAPTAIN SHAW ARE TALKING ...

"AND THE KRAKKEN'S NEST WAS FULL OF EGGS," SAYS BEN. "NO WONDER SHE HAS BEEN ATTACKING EVERYTHING. JONAH MUST BE STEALING HER EGGS!"

I DID A LITTLE CHECKING ON FRIENDS OF FISH.

JONAH MELVILLE IS NO FRIEND. HE TRAVELS THE WORLD POACHING RARE ANIMALS, THEN CRATES THEM UP AND SELLS THEM TO PRIVATE COLLECTORS.

"CRATES THEM UP?" SAYS BEN. "OH, MAN! WE'VE GOTTA STOP THEM. HE SAID SOMETHING ABOUT GOING BACK TO A CANNERY!"

MUMMY OR NOT, THAT BEAST IS MINE.

LET'S GO. I HAVE A SPARE BOAT DOWN AT THE DOCKS.

SHAW STILL WANTS TO CAPTURE THE KRAKKEN! MAX, BEN AND GWEN SPEED OFF FOR THE CANNERY, LEAVING SHAW STRANDED AT THE DOCKS.

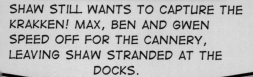

AT THE CANNERY, JONAH IS HELPING TO LIFT EGGS OUT OF THE LAKE.

CAREFUL, OR YOU'LL BE CLEANING UP THE WORLD'S MOST EXPENSIVE OMELETTE. AFTER WE SELL THESE BABIES, WE'LL BE KICKING BACK ON A BEACH IN THE BAHAMAS!

THE GANG ARRIVE AT THE CANNERY. BEN DECIDES IT'S TIME TO KICK SOME FRIENDS OF FISH TAIL! HE PRESSES DOWN ON THE OMNITRIX AND BECOMES ...

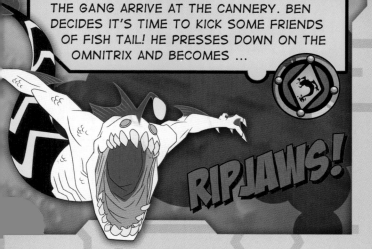

RIPJAWS!

THE KRAKKEN ARRIVES, AND SHE'S SPOTTED HER EGGS! JONAH HOPS INTO AN ARMED SUBMARINE.
HE DIVES UNDERWATER AND FIRES AT THE KRAKKEN. SUDDENLY RIPJAWS LOOMS INTO VIEW ...

YOU WANNA MESS WITH A MONSTER?

TRY ME ON FOR SIZE!

A HUGE BATTLE BEGINS, BETWEEN THE KRAKKEN, JONAH AND RIPJAWS. RIPJAWS IS TRYING TO RESCUE THE EGGS AND RETURN THEM TO THE KRAKKEN'S NEST, BUT THE KRAKKEN THINKS THAT RIPJAWS IS JUST ANOTHER ENEMY ...

AT LAST, RIPJAWS SNATCHES THE PRECIOUS EGGS FROM JONAH, AND GENTLY PLACES THEM AT THE BOTTOM OF THE LAKE.

JONAH IS CAUGHT BY THE KRAKKEN WHO CRUNCHES HIS ARMED SUBMARINE BETWEEN HER RAZOR-SHARP TEETH, AND DESTROYS IT.

THE KRAKKEN IS ABOUT TO GOBBLE JONAH UP ... BUT RIPJAWS GETS BETWEEN THEM BOTH.

THE KRAKKEN RETURNS TO HER EGGS AND NEST. MEANWHILE, RIPJAWS SWINGS ROUND, AND *SMACKS* JONAH IN THE FACE. THE DUDE'S OUT COLD!

RIPJAWS HANGS THE DAZED JONAH ON A PIECE OF WOOD STICKING OUT OF THE LAKE.

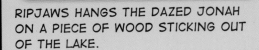

HANG HERE FOR A WHILE,

UNTIL THE POLICE FIND A NICE DRY CELL FOR YA.

HEARING A POLICE SPEEDBOAT APPROACHING, RIPJAWS DISAPPEARS ...

MAX AND GWEN ARE WATCHING FROM A PONTOON. SUDDENLY SHAW APPEARS, ROWING A DINGY TOWARDS THEM. HANGING UPSIDE DOWN INSIDE A NET IS RIPJAWS.

MEET THE CHARACTERS

BEN TENNYSON
TEN TIMES MORE TROUBLE THAN THE AVERAGE KID!

GWEN TENNYSON
RED-HEADED VOICE OF REASON TO HER COUSIN BEN

GRANDPA MAX
JUST A MILD-MANNERED GRANDFATHER – OR IS HE?...

VILGAX
ALIEN WARLORD WITH A REAL ATTITUDE PROBLEM

FOUR ARMS
PROOF THAT FOUR ARMS ARE BETTER THAN TWO

HEATBLAST
THIS ALIEN'S ON FIRE!